WEST YORKSHIRE ADVENTURES

Edited By Allie Jones

First published in Great Britain in 2017 by:

Young Writers
Coltsfoot Drive
Peterborough
PE2 9BF
Telephone: 01733 890066
Website: www.youngwriters.co.uk

FOREWORD

Welcome, Reader!

For Young Writers' latest competition we set pupils nationwide the challenge of creating their very own crazy creature mini saga, a story of up to 100 words with a beginning, middle and end – a hard task indeed!

I am delighted to present to you 'Crazy Creatures – West Yorkshire Adventures', a collection of crazily creative storytelling that will introduce you to a wonderful world of monsters and beasts born from the most inspired imaginations. Just like me you will be taken on all kinds of different adventures meeting these crazy creations and, I'm sure, will be enthralled by all the wonderful creatures you come across. From monsters that live under the bed to superhero beasts battling evil, this collection has a story for everyone.

I'd like to congratulate all the talented writers that submitted their work to the competition; it was such a pleasure to read all the wonderful stories. I hope that seeing their creatures brought to life in this anthology helps inspire these writers to produce more brilliant creative writing. Now, as you step back into the crazy world ahead, I hope you find as much enjoyment reading about these crazy creatures and their capers as much as I did.

Allie Jones

Burton Salmon Community Primary School, Leeds

Myles Robert Welbourne (10)	54
Isabella Diagostino Cummings (9)	55
Macey-Lou Hartley (9)	56
Sydney Webster (9)	57
Sophie Jessica Shearsmith (8)	58
Neo Conor (8)	59
Jennifer Summer Collins (7)	60
Georgia Grace Carrington (10)	61
Lyndon Snowden-Hicks (10)	62
Lydia Dixon-White (7)	63
Harry Gill (10)	64
Emily Kennedy (7)	65
Anz Fongmake (9)	66
Ellie Knowles (11)	67
Reuben Russell Holden-Clough (8)	68
Gabriel Bruce Witty (11)	69

Killinghall Primary School, Bradford

Asmaa Parveen (9)	70
Umar Ali (9)	71
Fatimah Al-Zahra (9)	72
Hanna Khalil (9)	73
Iqra Ahmed (9)	74
Malaika Farid (10)	75
Luckman Mohammed (9)	76
Imama Mubashar (10)	77
Anna Patience Mills (9)	78
Laiba Qazi (10)	79
Aaminah Ali (9)	80
Areebah Kausar (10)	81
Mohammed Luqmaan Khan (10)	82
Sufyan Ahmed (9)	83
Mahnoor Nabeel (9)	84
Ali Raza Muhammed (9)	85
Muhammed Yasir (9)	86
Muskaan Arzoo Khan (10)	87
Muhammad Tayyab (9)	88

Muskaan Jabeen (9)	89
Aliya Khan (9)	90
Alishba Noor Hussain (10)	91
Mohammed Awais (9)	92
Shayaan Abbas (9)	93
Wahaab Ali (9)	94
Harvey Lee Puckrin (10)	95
Ayaan Malik (10)	96
Hamza Iqbal (9)	97
Qasim Ahmed (9)	98
Usman Ali (9)	99
Saif Hussain (9)	100
Samarah Shah (10)	101
Selina Ali (10)	102
Sameer Basharat (10)	103
Maryum Anife (10)	104
Mahdiya Nurmohmed Shaikh (9)	105
Ibrahim Razwan (9)	106
Anas Tanveer (9)	107
Umairah Mehmood (9)	108
Dawud Ahmed (9)	109
Kanzul Imaan (10)	110
Sohaib Hussain (9)	111
Amna Bahadar (10)	112
Armaan Hussain (10)	113
Laiyba Hussain (9)	114
Alimurtaza Arfan (9)	115
Eiman Kauser (9)	116
Usman Qaiser (10)	117
Azaan Sarfraz (9)	118
Suleman Ali (9)	119

Paradise Primary School, Dewsbury

Khadija Abdelbadir (7)	120
Umaama Ali (7)	121
Aisha Bodhania (6)	122
Zainab Vali (6)	123
Hafsa Tukur (7)	124
Fatima Moosa (7)	125
Ahmed Musa Shoaib (6)	126
Humayra Patel (7)	127
Maariyah Moosa (6)	128

Muhammad Patel (6) 129

Springwell Leeds Primary Academy, Leeds

Kian Joe Salisbury (11)	130
Konneur James Dooley (11)	131
James T Sheridan (9)	132
Lewis Fletcher (9)	133

Victoria Primary School, Keighley

Aamna Ali (9)	134
Uthman Ali (10)	135
Alisha Zafran (9)	136
Benyamin Malik (9)	137
Ehsan Khurshid (10)	138
Mishal Hussain (9)	139
Muhammad Ismail (9)	140
Aaliyah Jamil (9)	141
Adam Hussain (10)	142
Juwairiyah Mahmood (9)	143

THE STORIES

Help!

Hoynsh and Zeph were practising 'creature cannonball' stunts. Hoynsh's see-through stretchy covering and sticky pads acted like rubber bands shooting them through the air like cannonballs. Suddenly Eddy arrived, an inquisitive boy. Zeph froze, so still in fact that Eddy mistook Zeph for a toy and dragged him up to his room, shutting the door behind him. Zeph pondered his escape. The door was locked and the open window too high. 'How am I going to get out?' Zeph snuffled, his 160 brownish, secret spines bristling. 'Wait, is that Cannonball Hoynsh I hear, wriggling up the door...?'

Aimee Dalby (9)

Wormdog's Big Mistake

One sunny day, a big bang happed on Strawberry Field Lane. It was Wormdog; brown and green. He was trying to get away from big-mouthed Wormcat. In the afternoon, Wormdog went out for a long walk. His long, squirmy tentacles twitched. Suddenly, from the corner of his eye, he saw Wormcat. Wormcat had followed him from Neptune. All this time, Wormcat had been looking for him. Wormdog was just about to wrap his tentacles around Wormcat, when Wormcat explained that he had been looking for him because he wanted to be his friend. So they lived happily ever after.

Holly Hurst (9)

Hooray For Cory!

132 million years ago, I, a brachydospilfirrel (a cross between a silky squirrel, a woolly wolf, a speedy spider, a daring dog and a brilliant Brachytrackdopen) woke up under the sand in the Sahara Desert.

Slowly, I climbed out of the burning sand and began to search vigorously for a water hole. I came across a snake who told me he was called Jeffrey. He led me to a herd of antelope. With one snap of his powerful jaws, he caught one. He offered me some. I tried it but I didn't like it, so carried on with my mission.

Francis Hein (9)

Bogle

My crazy creature is called Bogle and looks a bit like a potato with two legs that have been squashed, but it's a gross green colour! Bogle also has two big, round eyes that look like they're about to fall off his fat, ugly face. His favourite hobbies are fishing for pickles, ironing cats, smelling books and finally, eating glue. This grumpy, weak and unpleasant creature lives in your tumble dryers, so please be careful people and always check before going to bed because you never know what could be in there!

Freya Mae Webster (10)

Pong And Bong

One day, Bongy, a cute creature, was happily living on Planet Bong. Emerald-green trees, vibrant coloured flowers. Suddenly, the creatures from Planet Pong invaded. Sadly, they put a spell on their land and all the greenery turned dull. King Kong, the ruler of Planet Bong, tried everything he could but they were too strong. Amazingly, Bongy found that he had super powers. Excited and elated, he tested his powers. Turning invisible and squirting slime! He went face to face with Planet Pong. *Pow! Crash! Bang!* Finally, victory was achieved. Planet Bong was saved, thus Bongy the hero saved the day!

Ayesh Mohsin (10)
Allerton CE Primary School, Leeds

My Job Being A Spy!

One mysterious day, Liquorice Angel was on a mission. It wasn't any mission, it was a mission against her enemies, The Liquorice Haters. The Liquorice Haters are this group from my childhood who would always be jealous of her super power. Her super power was shooting liquorice out of her eyes and cheeks. Curious and prepared, she got her eyes and cheeks ready for shooting. She kept on floating and floating and no sign of The Liquorice Haters. Out of nowhere came The Liquorice Haters, *bang!* She swiped them out. So that's her job, being a spy.

Cheani Bussue (10)
Allerton CE Primary School, Leeds

The First Ever Word Fight!

Study Buddy flapped her trifling wings, picking up speed. She darted her eyes for any predators and immediately pricked her dyed, sharp ears.
Suddenly, a talking lion appeared out of nowhere, the king of the land of lost lions.
'What are you doing here?' growled Study Buddy.
'Going for a hunt,' said Kingston, shrugging his shoulders. 'You'll be good for dinner.'
Study Buddy narrowed her wide eyes and focused on a strong word. Obnoxious. She shouted it out loud. It hit Kingston on the head painfully. Kingston spiralled to the ground, falling, falling...

Manya Marwah (10)
Allerton CE Primary School, Leeds

The Hour Before

Swimming around the deadly sea, I saw fish hiding and that was very unusual. Zedro is a serpent-type creature that is brightly coloured and can transform into anything. Now with fish screaming, he knew there was something wrong. He swam as quickly as a bolt of lightning to the army and got ready for battle. Now they knew who it was, it was Destrucktor. 'It's been a long time, my old friend,' said Destrucktor.

'You used to be my friend,' muttered Zedro. 'What do you want?'

'I want everything you own.'

'Then we shall battle.'

Harvey Court (9)
Allerton CE Primary School, Leeds

The Mission

Lamentor was scuttling along, pulling his small, nailed paws out of the wet mud. Lamentor personally thought this was a waste of time, but the General thought differently. His spiky back bristled against the wind. Lamentor used his super detector nose to know that he was in a windy and wet place in England called Leeds. He was on a mission to find the rest of his species. Lamentor used his four eyes to think well. Suddenly, he heard a growling and the soft padding of paws. He turned and there was his enemy, Farsmen. Lamentor shuddered... this was bad.

Jasmine Taylor (9)
Allerton CE Primary School, Leeds

Venom

It all started like this...
Long ago on Mars, there was an alien called
Venom. He looked like an ugly, green doll with big
hair. His special ability was hiding in the shadows,
so aliens called him The Dark Fright. He took his
power for granted, using it for evil. Then one day,
Mars got destroyed, so he went on a ship to Planet
Earth. Once he arrived, he was clueless where to
go, but he had a good idea. His idea was to follow
the shadows for a place to live, but he couldn't find
one... until Joe came.

Zedekiah James (10)
Allerton CE Primary School, Leeds

Cleverspikes And The Terrifying Aliens

Cleverspikes was moving steadily across the roads of North America with his enormous, ski-like feet. Everyone disappeared from this terrifyingly tall creature with his pointy, shark-like spikes and massive, ginormous brain. He thought, *why are all these people running away from me?* As quick as a lightning bolt, a blue whale-sized UFO came zooming out of the colourless clouds. Everyone vanished. However, the monster froze. He had a curious thought but as the aliens rushed out, *beep, beep, beep* went the computer as they speedily and furiously attacked. Suddenly, an awesome, amazing, fabulous, spectacular thing happened...

Arnav Maniyar (9)
Asquith Primary School, Leeds

The Monster's Town

Suddenly, *boom!* The bomb fell and the monster's town got destroyed. The monsters ran for their lives as the ashes and buildings were going up in flames and fell apart. Quickly, Flibyls decided he wouldn't let this happen to the beautiful town where he lived. 'I am going to call in the Griffins (magical birds) so I can fly in and take back our town! I will return, hopefully!'

The amazing Flibyls dived in but was too late. Now no one would lay eyes on this town again. It got bombed once more. The monsters will remember Flibyls. *Boom!*

Oliver Beilby (9)

Asquith Primary School, Leeds

The Wrong Answer

The Wrong Answer was about to wake up but then just fell back to sleep because of his own fluffy fur. Thirty seconds later, he automatically woke up. The teacher, whose ear he was living in, had opened the first book to mark. He would only whisper the wrong answer once. This was a very hard job. His kind couldn't resist, they just couldn't, but they all knew that if they whispered more than once, they would always accidentally hypnotise the teacher to squish them. He just whispered twice. That's when it started to come... the terrifying finger was coming.

Robin Gill-Carey (10)
Asquith Primary School, Leeds

Untitled

Years ago, on the planet Jupiter, a monster so deadly and fierce was about to cause mischief. Tornado Destroyer was over 50 feet tall and could cause more damage than anything this universe had ever seen. In a terrible rage, he swept through Jupiter's surface whilst chomping through buildings and the creatures that were in them. Back on Earth, an astronaut called Brooklyn decided to put a stop to this terrifying beast and all the trouble he was making. So he flew as fast as a flash of lightning and landed on Jupiter, where he bravely defeated Tornado Destroyer.

Brooklyn Connah Lonsdale (9)
Asquith Primary School, Leeds

The Menacing Mixer Strikes

The Menacing Mixer blasted off at the speed of light in his pod. *Boom! Crash! Smash!* He wondered where he was. He looked up and saw... an eagle. It was coming towards him and he ran for his life! *Why am I running*, he thought. He shot the eagle with his machine pistol. He gobbled it in one! He found a city called Leeds. He sliced humans in half and guts went everywhere. He knocked the puny humans with his baseball bat and murdered them with his gun. He shape-shifted into a human and found his pod. He blasted off!

Pearce Changeur (10)
Asquith Primary School, Leeds

Boom!

Stormster is a very unusual-looking creature. It has webbed hands and a spiked tail. He was minding his own business when a Guzler swooped overhead. This made him angry. Suddenly, he was buried. Snoz helped him out. They chatted away. The next day, he ordered a meeting. At the monster table, Stormster was chair. A shark tried to eat them. *Boom!* But Stormster just punched it in the jaw. Stormster blew up with anger. The miniature thing had exploded like a nuke and everything was destroyed. What would happen next?

Miles Kitchen (9)
Asquith Primary School, Leeds

A Close Call For Blotto

Blotto, absorbed in his feast, is oblivious to the gathering storm. The sky blackens and dark clouds engulf the once beautiful coastline. The creature desperately abandons his meal, seeking sanctuary. Suddenly, Blotto's most feared enemy appears: a ravenous crocodile searching out prey. Abruptly, the crocodile gets the first strike, opening a gaping wound in the alien's leg. Blotto retaliates by transforming his limb into a hammer then uppercutting the face of his nemesis, catapulting him into the air. As the predator plummets down, Blotto absorbs the force and allows his razor-sharp claws to pass through the croc's grotesque figure.

Ned Pullen (10)
Baildon CE Primary School, Shipley

Experiment No 209 - The Triplet Tricksters

Mad scientist Frankenstein's experiment went wrong, horribly wrong. Whilst experimenting trying to build a monster of brute strength, he created a monster of the mind. Three of them! Each one perfectly identical. The beasts could trick the human mind by creating virtual realities, holograms and could even make you delusional. Darkness spread over Europe, for the age of tricking had begun. The Europol, SWATs, even police attack forces (fighter jets, armoured vehicles, attack choppers) can't take them down, but only themselves from the inside out. Global forces have come together to stop this madness. Will they succeed?

Connor Benjamin Holmes (10)
Baildon CE Primary School, Shipley

The Frappled Squater's Great Escape!

The angry Frappled Squater with its slicing sabered claws, muscles itself against the iron bars of the claustrophobic cage. The whirling helicopter ascends into the night sky with trap firmly affixed to its fuselage. Hours later, the scorching ground hits the cage. In the dead of night, Frappled Squater silently slices away the steel bars and scuttles towards the Siberian bound research aircraft. Once aboard, he nestles behind the scientist's equipment and waits for takeoff. On landing, cold, crisp air meets the aircraft. Frappled Squater seizes his chance, takes off across the ice back to his isolated cave and hibernates.

Luke Graham Dudley (11)
Baildon CE Primary School, Shipley

Boblax Meets His Worst Nightmare

Once, there was a wonderful and magnificent rainforest that suddenly got ferociously savaged by a greedy, selfish monster. On this very day, a deadly and disgusting, four-eyed beast rapidly sabotaged this amazing land. This atrocious event happened in the Amazon rainforest, as this disgraceful beast destroyed this fantastic part of Brazil. But luckily, there was one, one who was braver than all the rest called Boblax. He said to his companions in a very loud voice, 'Let's do this for our country,' before adding, 'and for our people.'

The battle was four days long and Boblax defeated the monster.

Max Paterson (10)
Baildon CE Primary School, Shipley

Roar

Roars! Ear-splitting roars echoed suddenly in the mysterious night sky! Sinister and deadly shadows towered over me. Hanging clouds, looming up above, covered the dreary, miserable sky. Then, in the distance, a vague outline appeared. Approaching, the image (a ghastly image) abruptly came to a stop. The red lasers beamed rapidly out of his vermillion eyes and pierced my soul, causing me to stare in awe. Reaching forcefully, he grasped my trembling arm. Not knowing what to do, I screamed for help...

Awaking from my coma, sweat dribbled unpleasantly, bit by bit, down my face. A nightmare?

Katie Ratcliffe (10)
Baildon CE Primary School, Shipley

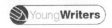

Screble The Cookie Monster

Once, there was a monster called Screble. He adores cookies and hates people. He once saw a boy walking down a back street, the boy was eating cookies and Screble threw a fireball at him then sneaked away. Screble isn't pleasant, he is a scruffy monster and very rough. Screble has super powers, he throws fireballs at people and has saliva venom. Screble especially loves Cadbury cookies. He always steals cookies from anywhere; shops, people and factories. So, Screble isn't a nice creature and he has favourites, he's not pleasant and can kill people. Really, Screble is a rebel.

Imaad Khadim (11)
Baildon CE Primary School, Shipley

Chompa, The Homework Eating Monster

Chompa, the word-eating monster, devoured the last bite of the crisp page. Nothing was left, not even a full stop. Suddenly, recognisable footsteps trudged towards him. Plunging his mucous body under the table, he hid. Obliterating all evidence, he licked the remains of the ink from his fangs. A body-shaking thud vibrated the wood above him. The human impatiently began searching for his masterpiece. Chompa had naively left his leathery tail protruding from his refuge. It was too late. The boy (as if caught in a hurricane) tumbled. There was an awkward silence and then they both locked eyes.

Oliver Robertshaw (10)
Baildon CE Primary School, Shipley

The Electrical Shock!

'Accidents have been happening because of power cuts, people have been saying they've seen aliens, but we know they don't exist. Is this true?'

As he was watching the news, being feared made him stronger and stronger. Electrical Eric, who has lightning bolts as body parts and is the colour of the scorching sun, has been stealing electric from panicked people. His darkest secret was kept deep inside, no one would ever find out...

It was soon pitch-black. Eric found himself wandering the streets like a mouse in the sewers. Will the human race survive? Will it be the end?

Amelia Grace Brooke (10)
Baildon CE Primary School, Shipley

The Disastrous Diglet Chase!

Dark clouds hovered over London. The bleak, barren wind howled infuriatingly, waking the city. A bitter, frosty breeze nipped at James' fingers as he pulled up outside the hotel. When he reached his room, James opened his briefcase... his beloved pet, a Diglet, wasn't there! This was a disaster! The secret of mythical beasts could be exposed! He knew exactly where to go... the jewellery shop, the Diglet's favourite place. He adored collecting valuables and stuffing them in his pouch! As he flew around the corner, the police appeared. Was it too late? Did he have time to save him?

Sophie Breen (11)
Baildon CE Primary School, Shipley

The Deadly Homework Destroyer!

Did you ever wonder what that grumbling sound is in the middle of English? No, it's not kids yawning. In the stock cupboard, that your teacher has, there is a monster hungry for homework!

One day, the creature was sneaking into somebody's bag to eat their homework. He didn't notice footsteps. The terrified creature dashed under a coat to hide his mischief, but they spotted a red foot. They screamed as the monster hurried out of the cloakroom and out of the antiquated door. To this day, people are missing homework and hearing groaning!

Could this monster still live on?

Poppy Brownnutt (10)

Baildon CE Primary School, Shipley

The Homework Dragons

One night many years ago, a legend was told that a six-winged mythical creature would devour any homework in sight. Only a few stories have been told about this and it was at my school.

In 2016, our class became raided with thousands of minuscule flying beasts, soaring up and down the corridors, in and out of the classrooms, gnawing on the delicious paperwork. In minutes of breathing crimson flames, the room burst into a volcano. Each fire alarm started ringing.

The dawn was breaking. The dragons glided back over the sunset to their nest (unaware that my homework survived).

Lucas Free (10)

Baildon CE Primary School, Shipley

Ravenous Razor Rapid

Razor Rapid lives in a cave next to a primary school, he likes to eat children!
Miss Ploppingson is a teacher and has been asked to investigate the mysterious disappearances of children. She starts at the school gates and hears a strange munching sound. She walks further, seeing a child's shoe covered in green slime. Miss Ploppingson follows the trail of slime. She finds an unusual cave. She walks into the cave nervously and sees a magical looking creature. Scared, she picks up a stick and goes to hit Razor Rapid but she's not quick enough and he eats her!

Charlie Driver (11)
Baildon CE Primary School, Shipley

The Mega Mocking Microbe!

Mr Bannoffe was very confused. He thought Ben had kicked the football onto the forbidden field, so how could Ben have written 'This school's a dump' on the whiteboard at the same time? Little did Mr Bannoffe know that amongst the shadows of the putrid school bins, (where all the children secretly threw their disgusting, inedible school dinners), lived the Mega Mocking Microbe and he was the one causing all the school's trouble. Eventually, the children trapped the malicious creature in a bowl of lumpy custard and from then on he troubled a different unfortunate school.

Isobel Loughran (10)
Baildon CE Primary School, Shipley

Quadrathon Quest

Pixieball is a microscopic creature. She doesn't look like much, but today she will try to defeat her arch-enemy, Quadrathon. If Quadrathon tries to walk in front of her, he will fail because she devours everything in her way. So she sets off on her quest to beat Quadrathon.

In the distance, she hears a loud crunch with her pixie, long ears. Could this be Quadrathon? Pixieball pauses, freezes, not to make a sound. Quadrathon is the stealthiest creature alive. Other appliances emerge from her body as she approaches him. She bites him, burns him, until there's nothing...

Honey Amelia Clarke (11)
Baildon CE Primary School, Shipley

Choco Warrior

Usually, chocolate bars wait on the shelf until they're bought, right? Not this one, it had a secret... a secret of being... a monster! Are you wondering how this creature got on Earth and where it's from? Well, it's from Gobble-Wobble and she appeared on Earth by falling out of her high-tech colourful spaceship. But the Choco Warrior had a dream to explore Planet Earth in all its glory! So that's what she did. She searched every country with detail until finally, she exclaimed, 'A shelf is big enough for me!' She went back home to rest... until next time.

Isabel Powell (11)
Baildon CE Primary School, Shipley

Katie's Hiccup Nightmare

Hiccup, hiccup! came from the bedroom. Katie (the poor girl) tried to think of a way to get rid of her hiccups. She was advised to hold her breath and nose but she gave up. None of the suggestions worked! She fell into a deep sleep...

Marching towards her was an evil-eyed, creepy-looking figure. She was so terrified that she gulped in horror. As the mysterious creature came close, a gloomy smirk spread across his face and hiccups flew out of his mouth. Immediately, she was so scared that she awoke. 'No hiccups!' Katie sang merrily, skipping around.

Philippa Kate Bartle (10)

Baildon CE Primary School, Shipley

The Electro Cyclops!

In the dust of the past, the Electro Cyclops travels through the anonymous world: quick as a gun; the speed of light; or fast as mankind.

The Big Eco Man, Electro's enemy, tries to reduce the use of electricity, but Electro tricks people by turning on lights and showers, or changing the heat.

The Electro Cyclops follows you everywhere, in every electronic device. He messes with you and the only way to stop him is to turn the world dark with no lights or electronics.

The Eco Man will be honoured for fighting the Electro Cyclops and become a hero.

Connor Jack Wilson (10)
Baildon CE Primary School, Shipley

Spotacular's Disaster!

Spotacular was soaring over cloudy New York as it became apparent to him that he was being watched. As he circled the sky, he saw the silhouette of a young child glaring up at him. 'There's a dragon!' the little boy screamed, excitedly. Spotacular knew he had to take this boy away to the floating island, he absolutely felt no doubt. He looked mischievous and was already spreading the word. Through furious wind, he swooped down like a cheetah. Before the boy could say another word, he took him! Was it too late or would Spotacular let him come back?

Anna Breen (9)
Baildon CE Primary School, Shipley

Brainless Bob

This extraordinary creature is Brainless Bob (BB). BB goes out with his mates for a few drinks. Scuffbag Scott, Toothless Tom and Piercings Paul drink and prance around, singing like a herd of cats and fall over. BB changes his hair more often than he changes his underpants, from blue to green, to pink, to purple. His stomach piercings are accompanied by a large tattoo of his ex-girlfriend, who he can't stand. His eight gold teeth arrived the day after he bungeed from a 4,000 foot bridge. There are no crazier creatures than human beings. Boy, are we strange!

Nell Grace Hepton (11)
Baildon CE Primary School, Shipley

Revenge...

Filus, a shape-shifter from Planet Alarbus, 2,000 Earth years away, teleported from his home town down to Planet Earth. He was following in the footsteps of his ancestors, who were captured by the wicked Earthlings and taken to a lab for investigation. Filus' magical power would ensure that the same thing would not happen to him! He could transform into whatever he wanted to be: an innocent cat taking a leisurely stroll, or an aggressive dog charging down an alleyway!
He headed to the small Yorkshire town of Baildon, bloodthirsty for revenge...

Will Savage (10)
Baildon CE Primary School, Shipley

Colin's Cunning Castastophe

Early one morning, Colin woke up, ready for another day of pranks.

The school bell had just rung, as his friends begged him for a mega-prank that the head teacher would never forget. Devilishly, Colin got to work!

He knew his victim would be a hard one to catch, especially as Colin was a large, scaly, purple alien! He hardly blended in with the kids. His slime bucket was ready, all lined up for the nerdy head teacher to come scurrying into his dreary office... but it wasn't Mr Beige, it wasn't him at all. It was the school inspector!

Dominic Horne (10)

Baildon CE Primary School, Shipley

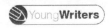

Platypie

Platypie, the platypus Gidemon, is a poisonous beast and the evolved form of Bibarel. It gained more speed by training and racing, so it could outspeed any Serperior.

It grew up in packs, hunting its prey by spitting poison. But it is also a peaceful creature, eating crops grown by itself. When disturbed, it scratches the attacker so strongly, it hurts the opponent to bleeding point and the enemy is poisoned in the stab.

Platypie was the most feared hunter of its time because it could hunt the Pokémon we know as legendary today.

Gideon Simpson (11)
Baildon CE Primary School, Shipley

Spike

Spike looks like a tall, prickly cactus. He is friendly and loves to make creatures laugh. He's the class clown, telling jokes and messing around.
One day, after going to a fair, he decides that he wants to do balloon modelling and make crazy creature balloons for his friends. The trouble is, every time he starts to blow the balloon up, it pops on his sharp points. What is he going to do? He decides to wrap himself in toilet roll until it covers his spikes. He looks just like an ancient Egyptian mummy! His balloons are epic, everyone laughs!

Sam Miller (10)
Baildon CE Primary School, Shipley

What Happens When You Eat All The Food?

Once lived a creature called Putrido. He came from a planet named Putridonous and was sent to Earth to be cared for by humans. He had a big mouth, short torso and many slimy, jelly-like legs so he could move around quickly to sneak to the fridge filled with lots of junk food he could devour.

One day, Holly (Putrido's owner) came home from work. When she opened the fridge door, nothing was left inside. So, she made an obstacle course for him to get to the fridge and, when she finished, Putrido tried it which gradually made him fail.

Leyani Hird (10)
Baildon CE Primary School, Shipley

The Midnight Monster

Midnight was approaching. Hetty slipped on her coat and tiptoed out of the silent house. Rain pattered deafeningly on her car as she sped through the town centre, out into the countryside. She did not know where she was going, nor did she know why she was. Suddenly, Hetty stopped. She had pulled over at a gloomy field. Stepping reluctantly out of her car, the poor woman trudged for what seemed miles. She felt her body reform. Fur sprouted on her skin, red horns grew from her head. There was no doubt about it, she had transformed into a monster...

Rawan Ali (10)
Baildon CE Primary School, Shipley

The Great Escape Of Googlebool

In a far, far away galaxy existed two planets. On the misty, dusty hillside of Danod, Googlebool's enemy planet, Googlebool was trapped in a cage. There were no guards around so he used his brains to activate his slime and slip through the bars; and he did it when everyone was sound asleep. On the way back to Zeptos, Googlebool's home planet, he saw a couple of guards and thought to himself, *this is a piece of cake.* He used his supersonic scream to knock out the guards. He found no guards so he just flew home.

Parth Sunil (10)
Baildon CE Primary School, Shipley

Bogalog

Bogalog has one eye and that eye can hypnotise you. If you look straight into that eye, you transform into something odd, perhaps a flip-flop, perhaps a book, perhaps a log! You never know... Bogalog can shape-shift, so watch out! He might be your pencil. Perhaps you didn't know that when you see something in the corner of your eye, then you turn around and it's not there, yeah, that's Bogalog. He disappears you see. He likes to scare people but not to their faces. He gets scared and disappears. Is that your pencil moving? Argh!

Sarah Silveira (10)
Baildon CE Primary School, Shipley

Matchalatcho And His Floating Brain

One day, a special creature, Matchalatcho from the Milky Way, decided to visit Earth. He was special because he had an extra brain that floated above his head and gave him special powers. He liked Earth but he also came across some bad people. He decided to stay and help the good people by using his special brain to magic any bad people to the Milky Way until they learned how to become good, then returning them to Earth. The people of Earth were grateful for Matchalatcho's help and they lived peacefully for the rest of their lives.

Henry Blakey (10)
Baildon CE Primary School, Shipley

Craze Ball To The Rescue

On a little planet called Boggle Oggle, disaster struck. A little monster (Craze Ball) was needed desperately for a number of reasons; his arch-enemy, Snowball, turned the planet to ice. People couldn't get out of their houses because there was too much snow. People from other planets were trying to take over and Snowball was turning people into ice. Craze Ball was the only one that could help for he has fire hair and can melt the ice. He can also make his arms stretch from planet to planet so he can save anyone that needs it.

Chloe Goodbold (10)
Baildon CE Primary School, Shipley

Larry Lamb And Lockers!

Larry Lamb loved hiding. One day, Larry hid inside a locker and a girl called Philippa found him. He was a lamb though! He shape-shifted into a tiny baby lamb. He speedily ran into the teachers' office and simply ate all the people inside! He ran around the school and gobbled up all the teachers in the classrooms. The children cheered happily as Larry also gobbled down their school work too! They took Larry to McDonald's but he wasn't that hungry after eating so much knowledge. Larry Lamb went home to rest forever.

Mia Taylor (10)
Baildon CE Primary School, Shipley

Collin And His Big Secret

Collin is an ordinary monster. He has five feet, a pointy tail and a humongous, fat nose. Collin lives in the North Carabian, at house number 24 Woodpecker Lane. His hobby is climbing. He uses his sticky spots to climb. When he is in danger, he uses his super pointy tail to attack. Collin, who enjoys life, also has enemies. His enemies are Luke, who likes football, and Rodrick who is a ninja. But Collin's biggest secret is that he just wants to be friends with Luke and Rodrick. Sadly, that will never happen for Collin.

Melody Myers (11)
Baildon CE Primary School, Shipley

Moving Shadow

On Thusday morning, the children of 6H were in for some bad luck. The patch of darkness in the corner of the classroom was there as usual. The students came laughing and chatting like usual, Mr Holliday shouted at them like usual. However, nobody noticed the dark patch moving...
Queen Axeidor was out to get the unfortunate class and was shifting from the black corner. Suddenly, the lights went out. The pencil cases disappeared. Then, nothing... she had gone too. But she will return, any day, any time...

Rebecca Hayward (11)
Baildon CE Primary School, Shipley

The Lost Tickle For Doedecon

Once, in a dingy town called Nepford, lived Doedecon who liked to tickle and jump one thousand metres onto another planet. He loved going into Nepford to scare his next victim with tickles and high jumps. His favourite place was the library, where he could shrink and hide in a book, preferably a green book so he could blend in with the cover. But one time, he jumped so high, he went through a time portal in deep space and was transported nine million years into the future, never to be seen again.

Amelia Yeadon-Bee (11)
Baildon CE Primary School, Shipley

The Demonstrative Demon

The Demonstrative Demon is a threat to the human race. He can turn into anything he wants. He was in a local Baildon school and decided to strike. The pupils had just come in from break and The Demonstrative Demon was ready to attack . As a child was writing in his English book, he decided to strike. He quickly turned into the pencil and scribbled all over the boy's work. The boy soon noticed, he knew he had to go. Quickly, he turned into a rubber and ran away. He has never been seen since.

Samuel Priest (10)
Baildon CE Primary School, Shipley

Goo Man's Great Escape

One day, Mr Goo went on a walk and never came back. On this walk, he was riding on his bike, practising for a competition. Mr Goo, who is friendly, kind and helpful, wants everyone to be kind to him. He wears a top hat and red and orange shoes. Whilst he was practising, he stumbled upon a cave and someone locked him in, never to be seen again. Luckily, he found his way out of it and then he was forced into hiding. Ten years later, he came out of hiding and lived a normal life again.

Flynn Collings (10)
Baildon CE Primary School, Shipley

The Wonders of Municorn

Municorn didn't know what to do! He didn't know where to go! He was lost. The sun was sweltering and making him bake and he walked until he froze. He looked around, then he found out what was circling him... it was an eagle on the hunt. He quickly turned invisible and as it was coming down to get him, Municorn shot a laser beam and scared the eagle away. After that, Municorn decided that he needed to get home, so he started to fly back to his homeland called big, blue Pluto.

Oliver James Hawksworth (10)
Baildon CE Primary School, Shipley

Big Nose Jim

Once upon a time, there was a boy named Jim who had the most gigantic nose you have ever seen. One day, whilst at the park of magic, he thought to himself, *I think I'll do a prank on all my friends!* So, whilst walking and thinking, he fell right on his nose yet he was flying and not falling because his nose held him up. People from all over the park would come to see him, although it was very, very hard for him to get down to the floor again.

Hannah Goulden (10)
Baildon CE Primary School, Shipley

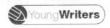

Electro And The Apocalypse

Tuesday 11th January, 2017: a radioactive ball crash-lands on Earth and triggers an apocalypse. There are only 20 survivors left on the entire planet! It turns out the ball that crash-landed was an alien called Electro from Mars! Yesterday the survivors went out looking for food and half of them were captured. Electro came out of nowhere. The survivors ran frantically back to the bunker, luckily with enough rations. Everyone was silent because they had lost their best friends. Nobody knows what happened to the captured survivors but they do know that Electro is still out there waiting patiently...

Myles Robert Welbourne (10)

Burton Salmon Community Primary School, Leeds

Jelly Bean Mania

Once, a pencil called Bobble, who lived in a pencil case, had a magnificent owner called Izzy. The girl kept jelly beans in her case and she didn't know they were evil. These creatures were called Human Beans, the head of them was called Maleficent and he was tempted to steal Bobble's bobble on the tip of his horn. Human Beans loved bobbles because they ate them and this bobble tasted of chocolate. When Bobble was asleep, Maleficent sneaked cautiously into Bobble's bed and *zap!* Maleficent had been rubbed out! 'Yay! Bobble saved the day!' screamed the pens. 'Hero Bobble.'

Isabella Diagostino Cummings (9)

Burton Salmon Community Primary School, Leeds

The Shape-Shifter

One day, a young girl called Lucy was walking home from school. Suddenly, she heard a rustling noise coming from a bush. She decided to run to it but, even before she got there, a shape-shifter jumped out at her.

'Argh!' Lucy screamed.

'Blob Glob,' replied the shape-shifter. 'Will you be my friend?'

'Only if you don't eat me,' answered Lucy.

'I won't.'

Lucy suddenly had a thought, *how will I keep you away from my parents?* When they got home, Lucy tried to keep her parents from seeing him but it was too late...

Macey-Lou Hartley (9)
Burton Salmon Community Primary School, Leeds

Struck Dead

One starry night, above the violent graveyard, a ghost named Nobody gazed upon the full moon. As he gazed, he had a magnificent idea! Or for him, he did... one word - kill! Since when he was alive, he got bullied and killed by Simon Cowell! Now it was time for revenge...

The next night, Simon walked through the cemetery. After one blink, dead! A little girl, Sydney, knew just what to do, find a hoverboard but where? The mayor has one (in case you didn't know, Nobody lives in the sky cloud). What could possibly go wrong?

Sydney Webster (9)
Burton Salmon Community Primary School, Leeds

Dancie The Disco Diva

Deep down in a ghost-seeking basement lives a rather odd creature named Dancie! He dances all night like he is at an 80s disco and will not stop for the world. Dancie is my best friend plus he plays the greatest rock and roll tunes in the universe! He never feels lonely as he has me to comfort him and I have him to comfort me. His favourite phrase is certainly 'disco in the dark makes you an 80s man!' However, when the disco ball drops and the light comes through, you will see another side of your disco friend...

Sophie Jessica Shearsmith (8)
Burton Salmon Community Primary School, Leeds

Voice In The Dark

On Halloween an unconfident teenager went to an abandoned pizzeria and got lost in the darkness and heard wires and a strange voice that said, 'Do you want to play with me?'
He whimpered, 'No!' It put its face and body in the light. It stared at him so he ran away and called SWAT and, when SWAT got there, they imprisoned it and it turned into a granny. The boy threw a human and it ate the human. So they called a repair man and he powered it off and took its power source and then he destroyed it.

Neo Conor (8)
Burton Salmon Community Primary School, Leeds

The Magic Day

When Shape-Shifter came back from school he looked around. This was not his house, he was at his old house in Shape-Shifter Land where he was living but he ran away. Anyway, he didn't like it there, they didn't treat him nicely. So that's why Shape-Shifter came to England. He couldn't believe it because he had to go to school with humans but at least he really enjoyed it. He had lots of friends at his school. He had a wander about then he got captured and he went to prison but he got out of prison and went home.

Jennifer Summer Collins (7)
Burton Salmon Community Primary School, Leeds

Unicorn

Once upon a time, a thing called Unicorn was kicked off an island because he was mischievous and they thought he was a demon. He was pink so he was made fun of.

A few years later, he crashed his rocket and met a boy called Billy who gave him a home. Unicorn said, 'What is your name?'

'Billy,' he replied. He was so happy to have a home. Billy lived in York, slap bang in the middle.

After a few years, Unicorn's rocket was fixed and he flew away back to Planet Zog never to be seen again.

Georgia Grace Carrington (10)

Burton Salmon Community Primary School, Leeds

The Nightmare In The Hospital

One day, the council wanted to reopen an abandoned hospital but there was a problem. There was a monster inside! His name was Spooker. Then the monster council wanted to get rid of him so they went in but Spooker tried to persuade them not to reopen it. Then the spooking games began. The maleficent monster set traps so they would be scared away. Then the monster got an idea to build a spaceship to escape and then cause more mischief in space with his new friends. And then he was never to be seen again...

Lyndon Snowden-Hicks (10)
Burton Salmon Community Primary School, Leeds

The Mars Wonder

Wiggler was on Earth when he nearly got hit by a car. Someone luckily just saved him. He walked off and found himself at a space station but he couldn't get in. Wiggler walked by the park, he wanted to fly home but he said to himself, 'It's my birthday!'
It was Christmas on Earth. He hadn't found a rocket yet but he had to find one. Later, he went to make one. He made a rocket and that was as sticky as a slug. He started the engines, turned on the radio and the rocket landed on Mars.

Lydia Dixon-White (7)
Burton Salmon Community Primary School, Leeds

Danger In Space

Once there was an alien named Spike. He was going to Mars to sign a treaty with them. On the journey, he hit a space centre. The pod couldn't move, the engines were fried. So, he climbed into the space centre to find parts to mend them. The floorboards were squeaky and rusty, it looked like it had been attacked because the engine room was gone. Then, all of a sudden, it sounded like a ship flying. It was the pod going to Mars. Then, *bang!* A big attack ship! Spike made a jump and landed on the pod.

Harry Gill (10)
Burton Salmon Community Primary School, Leeds

Fluffy's Adventure

Fluffy was a very fluffy, cute alien. She lived with her mummy and daddy on Sun Dog planet. She really liked her planet.

One day, she fell out of her planet and landed on Pluto. She had never seen Pluto before. She tried to jump onto her planet but she landed on Earth and she saw a rocket. She got inside, it was very big. She got strapped in and she flew off. She got home but she couldn't find her house so she had to look around the planet. She found her house and she was very, very happy.

Emily Kennedy (7)
Burton Salmon Community Primary School, Leeds

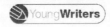

Fizzy The Clever Creature And The Dragon

One hundred years ago there was a creature called Fizzy. He was friendly and crazy. One hundred years later, Fizzy became the king. Everybody loved him. One day, there was an old, creepy dragon called Creepy because he was creepy and scary and not playful. He was not friendly. Creepy came to Crazy Creature Land. Everybody was not happy. Everyone told Fizzy about it. Fizzy was thinking and had an idea. Fizzy asked Creepy for a fight and Fizzy won. Everybody was happy and it was a happy ending.

Anz Fongmake (9)

Burton Salmon Community Primary School, Leeds

The Traumatising Jungle Animal

The crazy jungle animal loves to eat horrific bugs and hates to leave the jungle. When he leaves the jungle, he screams and shouts and lets it all out. He would go for a walk or to a horrific, horrible trail. The jungle animal hates spiders and emus and also doesn't like the one meal he gets every night because he doesn't have strength to cook it because he hates cooking. It ended up he had a jungle camp mate called Martin. He loved to cook so he cooked all of the lovely meals for camp.

Ellie Knowles (11)
Burton Salmon Community Primary School, Leeds

The Life Of Monster

Once upon a time, there was a kid called Red. He had a monster on his team called Pugachu. He got given a quest to find a tewmew. Once he found it he would become a monster master. Then he had to go to a city, to battle a gym leader and he won. He started to run, he stopped and got his bag then he dashed out and saw a squirie and he threw a monster ball. It broke out the first time and then he caught it, he then went onto a city, called Plunjer City.

Reuben Russell Holden-Clough (8)
Burton Salmon Community Primary School, Leeds

He Came From Mars

Tumbling towards Earth, the spacecraft landed badly damaged. Fisgog the alien from Mars was forced to shape-shift into a human and look for parts to repair his craft. So he set out and he went to a scrap yard. He was in luck, he found some of the things he needed but not all so went to a different yard and found all the parts. So, will he get back to Mars? Maybe not...

Gabriel Bruce Witty (11)
Burton Salmon Community Primary School, Leeds

Mr Treelogs Saves The Day...

Mr Treelogs tried to think with his wooden brain but L'o-g's didn't like laughter and happiness. He wanted to rule the world. Nobody wanted L'o-g's. He got really mad. He was ruining everything! Mr Treelogs had to do something. He tied a string to two trees and put banana peels in front.

'You will never defeat me!' said L'o-g's.

'Yes I will, you beast!' said Mr Treelogs.

L'o-g's tripped over the string and slipped on the bananas. He was thrown into outer space.

'We won't be seeing you again,' said Mr Treelogs.

'No we won't. Never again!' said the people.

Asmaa Parveen (9)
Killinghall Primary School, Bradford

Heart Crush

On a rainy day in Chicago, at the Scaredy Cat Centre, Roariana and Bratney were walking and stopped when a mysterious boy walked past them. They started fighting over him. DJ Wartie Claws broke them up. 'Why don't you two have a sing off?' he suggested.

Roariana started to sing grumpily, 'Ghoul you give me feelings never...'

'Stop!' screamed Crush. He was wearing a face mask and was peeling it off. 'I'm back!' shouted Crush in his evil deep voice.

'You monster!' shouted Roarinana

'We're monsters!' said Bratney.

'Not for long!' screamed Crush. 'See ya, suckers...'

Umar Ali (9)
Killinghall Primary School, Bradford

The Vexed Rockstar!

On a typical eerie day, in Rolling Rockstar Land, there lived a gentleman named Grumpy Not! Many fearful and ghostly things happened in the land. At midday, Grumpy was participating at a concert because of his admiration of singing. 'Why isn't anyone coming to my concert!' Grumpy screamed with vex. Later that day, people started to enter this concert.
'Ha!' sniggered the bullies and as they were saying this he was getting greater...
'I can sing!' he cried.
Surprisingly someone offered him a year's supply of children's stationery. After it all finished he killed everyone... It ended in a catastrophe.

Fatimah Al-Zahra (9)
Killinghall Primary School, Bradford

Pengess' Tale

Once there was a girl named Pengess, she had a unibrow and parts of her body electrocuted people. 'Oh no I don't want to experience that day again!' Now you probably want to know what that day was. Well guess what? You won't know till later. OK the day is Bullying Day where everyone bullies Pengess. 'Help, somebody help!'
'We better go and help her. I know, let's tell the king.'
'Sir, everyone is bullying Pengess, hurry!'
By the way Pengess is the king's daughter.
'Stop everyone! Stop bullying Pengess!'
Everyone apologised and lived happily with Pengess.

Hanna Khalil (9)
Killinghall Primary School, Bradford

Hoot Hoot Infinity And The Golden Twig

One day Hoot Hoot Infinity was soaring across the countryside. Later, he flew back to Twitter World to meet Twitter-Woo. When they met the heir was announcing, 'We have seen a vision that the Evil Guardian is to steal the Golden Twig!'

Everybody gasped in shock. Later Twitter-Woo and Hoot Hoot Infinity saw the Evil Guardian stealing the Twig. 'Stop, it's not yours,' they shouted.

'Who's going to stop me?' he shouted.

'We will have a race to decide.'

Whilst they were getting ready the Evil Guardian grabbed the Golden Twig from the supporting cushion and ran away with it...

Iqra Ahmed (9)
Killinghall Primary School, Bradford

Breezy Bella Vs Thunder Bolt

Breezy Bella had just finished work. She loved to help the poor and needy. As soon as her wings started to fly, someone grabbed her by the hand. 'Hey, who is this?' exclaimed Breezy Bella. But then she could sense danger. 'I know it's you Thunder Bolt!' screamed Breezy Bella.
'Well guessed Bella!' laughed Thunder.
It was night and Bella could hear Thunder snore. She sent a message about what had happened to her friend Breezy Bee. After five minutes, Breezy Bella broke free and locked Thunder in the cupboard. They had done it! But will Thunder Bolt stay captured...?

Malaika Farid (10)
Killinghall Primary School, Bradford

Master Gooey And His Enemy

Once upon a time Sir Gloom ruled the land of Greenea and told everyone to choose the right thing to do. This is Sir Gloom, he rules the land of Greenea but he can be a little bit bossy to people.

'Hi, what are you doing here?' said Sir Gloom.

'I'm just giving this man a tour around he house,' replied Swag Gloom.

'Shh, what's that noise?' said Sir Gloom.

'Haaa-waaa! Oh noo!' cried Swag Gloom. 'Save us!' Gooey Gloom speared him with his sharp, pointy arrow in his chest and he put him down.

'Hip, hip hooray!' they cheered.

Luckman Mohammed (9)
Killinghall Primary School, Bradford

Junorika Saves The Day

Junorika was a hero in Slavania Island. Whenever there was trouble, he would save the day. Slavania Island was a busy place. One day something didn't seem right to everybody, so they asked Junorika. He said, 'Everything is perfect.' Maltasa was an evil emperor who had put a spell on everybody. When Maltasa found out Junorika was going on holiday he decided to invade. It was going amazingly until Slyvah called Junorika to help out. Junorika turned into a human and tricked Maltasa that Venomly Shadow needed him but on the way he made a trap and off he went...

Imama Mubashar (10)
Killinghall Primary School, Bradford

Frogoneye And The Crown Of Jewels

Frogoneye looked up at the lustrous palace in awe. Just then his friend Boo-Boo came and said hello. After that the queen of Eyenana sounded her horn. She announced, 'Some of my jewels have gone missing. Keep an eye on anything suspicious!' Boo-Boo went to see Frogoneye because he was being suspicious. Boo-Boo found out that Frogoneye wanted to... steal the crown jewels! Boo-Boo got locked up. Frogoneye stole the crown jewels. The queen unlocked Boo-Boo. Boo-Boo ran up the hill to the palace. Frogoneye stepped out of the palace. Frogoneye was very surprised Boo-Boo was standing there...

Anna Patience Mills (9)

Killinghall Primary School, Bradford

Five-Eyed Gobble Gubby's Revenge

Five-Eyed Gobble is the most evil of evil creatures on Crazy Planet. He is very mean and wanted to take revenge on Whippy Noona and everybody else. Five-Eyed Gobble came and screamed 'I'm here!' He sprayed poisonous goo everywhere. He ruined everyone's things, he did this to take revenge. Whippy Noona had a plan to take Five-Eyed Gobble's goo away. She tricked him to come to the park. When he came, Whippy Noona took his goo powers away with her fire power. He was the worst slave for Whippy Noona. She made him suffer like he made everyone else suffer.

Laiba Qazi (10)
Killinghall Primary School, Bradford

Revenge Of Medusa

There once was a city called London. It was nice and peaceful there until Medusa and Melani showed up on television. They terrified humans by telling them where Powerman was. When Powerman heard this he knew what Medusa was trying to do, but he didn't know about Melani. Days passed and humans were wondering where he was for they were going to be turned to stone. Finally, Powerman had found out about Melani. 'I'm going to defeat you!' Powerman shouted. Melani screamed, 'Never!'
Powerman defeated her by believing in himself. He now started to believe in himself.

Aaminah Ali (9)
Killinghall Primary School, Bradford

Henry The Horrid Homework Hogger!

Henry the Horrid Homework Hogger lives on the Earth after being exiled from Boggontina (his planet). Since then he's always moody. One day, he hopped into a school and heard someone say, 'NASA has discovered a new planet called Boggontina!'

Henry started to cry. His race can't survive if humans know about them. Henry had an idea! He made a potion using a piece of Boggontina and spilled it into outer space. Suddenly a new planet appeared! The Boggons could move to it! He soon discovered his fire power then he went back to Boggontina as king after introducing homework.

Areebah Kausar (10)
Killinghall Primary School, Bradford

Another Planet!

Mr Pusanand is king of Goopiter. Dreadful things happen if the Gooster is around. Gooey is the most evil, he can shape-shift. Angrily there's someone kidnapping his brother. The kidnapper is from Godranus. He told him to stay away. In the newspaper unusual things have happened. Goopy was the angriest man alive today. When he woke up he heard screaming. People were melting. He wished for the Gooster but it disappeared. Now everyone in Goopiter was screaming. There was an agent from Godranus, he was the king of the new evil universe. The villagers screamed, 'Hooray!'

Mohammed Luqmaan Khan (10)
Killinghall Primary School, Bradford

Charizar Vs Mega Race

'Hello, it's me Charizar, I'm flying in the sky and looking at Charizar Land. One day I was fighting Mega Race the world's best fighter, he's very good.'

One night someone was lurking in the shadows, he went step by step, he saw nobody and then he heard a laugh. 'Ha-ha, ha-ha.'

He said, 'Who is that grey ninja?'

'Never enter the temple of doom. Ha-ha, ha-ha!'

'You will never get away with this!'

Then Mega Racer arrived. 'I challenge you to a battle.'

Charizar won!

Sufyan Ahmed (9)
Killinghall Primary School, Bradford

Revenge Of Deb

Deb went to his caretaker Luke's house. The people were screaming and shouting help because Ublo, Deb's enemy, had come. Finally, Luke heard muffled sounds as Luke and Deb got out of the house. Soon people were in Deb's long hands safe and sound. Luke got Ublo's machine gun to change the gel from bad to obeying orders. Next, Ublo started obeying orders.

'Ublo get on your tractor and drive away!' So he did.

Luke invited everyone to the feast. Everyone enjoyed the feast especially Deb. He was proud of himself and Luke. The people were not scared anymore.

Mahnoor Nabeel (9)
Killinghall Primary School, Bradford

Sergeant Lick's Adventure

Sergeant Lick was coming in from a stroll at Pluto Park. Then his mum called him to go shopping. He got in his spaceship and someone or something came zooming and brushed past Sergeant Lick's ship. It messed up the wiring and it crashed. He landed on Earth. Then someone called Leo came and explained he'd had the same problem.
Then they found some food but the evil mice wouldn't let them have it. 'Let's make a trap!' said Leo.
They made a trap, it worked. 'Nice one,' said Sergeant Lick. They tucked in, but how would they get back?

Ali Raza Muhammed (9)
Killinghall Primary School, Bradford

The Destroyer

The Destroyer Land is the most magical place ever and is the most destroyed place. The Destroyer won't let it be fixed. Every day he checks if if there is anything that's fixed. He creeps into the room and if anything is fixed he breaks everything. Early one morning he saw his land was fully fixed, he was very angry, 'Who has done this?' he shouted angrily. 'I will get revenge!'

That night he hid behind the bushes looking for the culprit so he could destroy his work. There he was. The Destroyer captured him, 'Yes, my revenge is complete!'

Muhammed Yasir (9)
Killinghall Primary School, Bradford

Zaydok's Journey

My crazy creature is Zaydok. When the land was attacked, the king said, 'I will kill them!'
His wife said, 'Be careful, I love you and what about our baby Zaydok?'
'Oh no,' said the king, 'The baby is not safe!'
Soon after, the enemy attacked and captured the mother. However, before she was captured, she hid Zaydok to save him from the enemy. As Zaydok grew up he longed to meet his mother. When he turned 18 he was given a sword. So, he went and defeated the enemies who captured his mother, rescued her and returned home safely.

Muskaan Arzoo Khan (10)
Killinghall Primary School, Bradford

We Are The Best!

In the peaceful town there was a dragon, Crunching Chartoise. He wanted to become the best with Tayyab. They went out to find a battle. They nearly crashed into a mountain but survived. There was nobody there! He found everyone hiding. Then he looked up, he saw a huge dragon. They had a fight and Chartoise was losing. He used his brain and was fast. He headbutted the dragon. The dragon fell and fainted. His friend was back to normal. They screamed, 'We are the best in the universe!' They don't know what is coming straight to their quiet town.

Muhammad Tayyab (9)
Killinghall Primary School, Bradford

Trying To Destroy The World

Once there was a huge army of robots that were in control of an evil person called Darth Mayhem. One robot was called The Half-Man Robotizer. Darth Mayhem was going to destroy him for being lazy. Then a superhero called Thunder Girl came and froze Darth Mayhem and took the robot home. The same thing happened each day and the weather kept on growing in Crazy Land and York. Finally, Thunder Girl made her choice and took Darth Mayhem to jail. Darth Mayhem said, 'Don't leave me here!'
She said, 'I have to.' Thunder Girl took the robots home.

Muskaan Jabeen (9)
Killinghall Primary School, Bradford

Mondona The Blue Mermaid

Mondona was in stress. She swam in circles with her blue tail. She couldn't find her tail polish. She spent two or three hours trying to find it. Afterwards, she took a break and then started to search for her tail polish again.

Hours later, Ruby (Mondona's magic mirror) woke up. She said, 'I saw Hazel going into your bedroom and she took your tail polish!'

Mondona angrily swam to Hazel's bedroom and told her to give it back. Hazel knew she had to give it, so she gave it back. Then Mondona decided to share it with Hazel.

Aliya Khan (9)
Killinghall Primary School, Bradford

Dealia Saves The Christmas, Hooray!

Happily, a mythical creature called Dealia lived in a land called Snowyland. Snowyland has snow and boutiques. Dealia was singing on Christmas Eve and she heard an evil laugh. She looked, nobody was there, she carried on. An old man wanted all the presents in the world. That night the man dressed up as Santa and stole all the presents. That same night Dealia saw him so she made the man deliver all the people their presents and then sent him to jail.

Thirty-five years later the old man got out of jail and said sorry to everyone in Snowyland.

Alishba Noor Hussain (10)
Killinghall Primary School, Bradford

Revenge Of Powerman

Cyclops ran as fast as he could with his giant feet, one step took him 200 metres. He looked tired and sweaty. Cyclops had red skin and he was running at the speed of light. The street was like an audience watching him as he kicked Kangaroo. Sicksammi went along and they got Bella, people call her Bouncing Bella because she's fat. Suddenly the sky turned black and Cyclops shouted angrily, 'Why are you here? I defeated you once and I'll do it again. Your weak spot is in your stomach.' Cyclops punched him and he was never seen again.

Mohammed Awais (9)
Killinghall Primary School, Bradford

The Big Problem

Bogey Mogey Man is big and green. His enemy is Fire Ball. Bogey Man was sitting down. He went for his early morning walk. He took a long time but finally came back.

Fire Ball, his enemy, was coming to invade Earth. 'Oh no,' said Bogey Man.

Fire Ball was from Mars but one day they got into a fight. Bogey Man threw bogies on him. Fire Ball got angry but actually he wanted to be friends. 'Oh please can you be my friend?' said Fire Ball.

Finally they became friends forever and also they lived together forever and ever.

Shayaan Abbas (9)

Killinghall Primary School, Bradford

Evil To Pleasant

On Tuesday the blood-sucking vampire came out from Antarctica to find some frozen food. He found somebody's home. He was going to suck the person's blood but he did not do that. He thought that there was nobody to stop him but there was! They were superheroes. Then he went nasty, foul and evil. He started shooting ice cream - it was horrible poison ice cream. Soon Devil Ice Cream Dabber got hit by a massive truck. Then a truck came super fast. At the end Cleany hit Devil Ice Cream. He went pleasant and paid everyone so they were happy.

Wahaab Ali (9)
Killinghall Primary School, Bradford

Bonzo's Penguin

Magic Land is a peaceful and clean place. Bonzo loves penguins so if anyone robs them he will laser their legs off. Early one morning Bonzo saw footprints around his house. Bonzo had just come from his jog and he noticed one of the penguins had gone and shockingly, his igloo was destroyed too. He hid behind a tree and he followed the criminal back to his base. Bonzo dodged all the traps and captured the criminal. 'Give me my penguin!' shouted Bonzo.
'OK,' said the criminal.
Then Bonzo went home with his precious penguin.

Harvey Lee Puckrin (10)
Killinghall Primary School, Bradford

Burglar Steals Christmas From Greandel

Stunningly Dark Land is not a clean land it's full of junk and if anyone tries entering, the Greandel will lock them up forever. The Greandel went to sleep and something happened, a burglar arrived and stole Christmas and wanted it for himself. He went home and slept while there was time for Greandel to get the presents. Greandel had hidden because he'd seen something move but he just went home and opened his presents and Greandel came back and made him sing a song, 'The Wheels on the Bus'. Greanel had a great time. The best.

Ayaan Malik (10)
Killinghall Primary School, Bradford

Untitled

Long, long ago there was a person called The Body Swapper. He was the king of all planets. The Body Swapper had one enemy called Hamton and he was begging to be king. The Body Swapper said, 'Your powers are too weak.'
Then Hamton said, 'Let me test my powers on you!' The Body Swapper said in anger, 'Your powers are too weak.' Suddenly he shot Hamton with abominable wither skills. Soon Hamton began to fade and die. So the Body Swapper buried him in the middle of his own planet. He was never seen again.

Hamza Iqbal (9)
Killinghall Primary School, Bradford

Civil War

One day there was a crazy creature called Poisner. His name was The Camouflage Poisner. There was a faraway land where the Poisner and his brothers Mike and Tyson had been buried in the sand by humans, that's why Poisner hated humans. Poisner and his brothers found the way out. 'Come on guys, you remember what the humans said. They want a war with us. Shall we accept?' said Poisner. 'No way!' said the brothers.

When the humans came the crazy creatures shot them and everybody lived happily ever after.

Qasim Ahmed (9)
Killinghall Primary School, Bradford

Untitled

Once there lived a horrible king called Selfish Sammy. He was king for three years but no one liked him. Suddenly, a storm blew the land, some goblins came and took the people from Gloomy Woomy Land, except for the king! The king had to do something. He thought until he had an idea. 'I am going to save my people.' So straight away he went to Goblin World and said, 'I will give you money if you reprieve the people.'
The people came and celebrated with the king. The king was never selfish again and the people were happy.

Usman Ali (9)
Killinghall Primary School, Bradford

Bog And The Surprise

Once there was a horrifying little, ugly monster. Nobody liked him. Monsters would pass by every day and look at him disgusted. Suddenly, he had a terrific idea. He could do something amazing. He was waiting for a monster to hypnotise. He waited for so long. *Why isn't anyone passing by?* He got up and started walking to his cave but then he found a note saying that he could find his destiny. The note told him to go to the cemetery. So he went to the cemetery and saw no one there. *Oh no, was that a false note?*

Saif Hussain (9)
Killinghall Primary School, Bradford

Ror Ror Land

Rouvent lives in Ror Ror land. A land that's creepy and spooky. She has snake hair, swirly eyes, she can float and turn invisible. When Rouvent kills people, they come back to life, walk funny and have eyes that are red. They were turning into zombies! 'Finally I've found out what the zombies are allergic to!' said Rouvent happily. Shockingly it worked and they finally died. When they were burnt she threw them into a river full of sharks, octopus, jellyfish, squid, poisonous pufferfish and stingrays.

Samarah Shah (10)
Killinghall Primary School, Bradford

Untitled

Mean Land is an ugly mysterious place. There is a colour throughout the breeze that makes it an unhappy place. Also there is litter everywhere. 'Who did this?' shouted Deadly Fairy angrily. So one night when everyone was in bed she turned invisible and was looking for whoever was littering everything. She hid in the bushes and followed the criminal to his base. She dodged all the traps and then she captured the criminal. She made him clean and build all the hospitals. Everyone lived happily ever after but not the criminal.

Selina Ali (10)
Killinghall Primary School, Bradford

Untitled

Spickland is a magical, beautiful land with many mysterious things going on there. In Spickland there is someone called Jeff. One morning Jeff saw one of his bags, which was loaded with gold, had gone.
The next morning Jeff was shocked because all of his bags of gold had been stolen on purpose. That night he went invisible and went to everyone's house and he finally found the gold. Jeff was so happy because he found the bags. He lived happily ever after and his enemies had learned a lesson not to steal money.

Sameer Basharat (10)
Killinghall Primary School, Bradford

Sweety The Sweet Lover!

Sweet Land is sanitised and majestic. Sweety always make sure no one is taking her sweets. She has a fragrance. At midday she steals sweets and if she sees anyone apart from her with sweets, then she will snatch them away and eat them herself.

The next day she went to the shop and all the sweets were gone. 'Where are all my sweets?' shouted Sweety angrily. That night, Sweety hid behind a bush and caught the culprit. She told him to pay back all the sweets. Early next morning the criminal gave them all back.

Maryum Anife (10)
Killinghall Primary School, Bradford

Untitled

Fireball Land is a land full of lava but in the East there is a lot of water and water is bad. Every day Fireball looks outside and people are getting bullied and some are taken away. The bigger kids hit them and then bad things happen. Fireball gets angry. Early one morning Fireball got up to have tea. He went to the window and said, 'Oh dear! These kids are getting bullied!' He shouted and in the end Fireball taught them a lesson. 'Don't be nasty because you will hurt other people's feelings!'

Mahdiya Nurmohmed Shaikh (9)

Killinghall Primary School, Bradford

Skylands Under Attack

Skylands is a magical world of wonder and adventure. Casandra is the darkest portal master in Skylands. She likes to torture the good so she hates the Skylanders. On that day Casandra headed towards Skylander Academy to retrieve her book of spells. Surprisingly Casandra and Goldy (golden queen) met at break. 'Yes!' Casandra shouted. The Skylanders stopped Casandra and Goldy. Both of them went into the forest and were very frustrated. 'We shall do a sneak attack at night. Ha-ha-ha-ha!' said Goldy loudly.

Ibrahim Razwan (9)
Killinghall Primary School, Bradford

Mini Mancraft And Bubble Dwarf

There was a planet called Saturn and there were two monsters. One was called Mini Mancraft and the other Bubble Dwarf. They were blue. They liked to eat paper and do bad stuff. There was a big school and the two monsters went in and went to the children's books. The children came in and Miss Mancraft went into someone's book bag. She saw the monster who was eating all the paper. They all ran. Bubble Dwarf was sad because no one came to the school again and the school shut down forever.

Anas Tanveer (9)

Killinghall Primary School, Bradford

Is It The End Of The World?

There was a creature called Evil Cyclops Butt Dave. He was on the toilet and was in his spike ball formation waiting for a human to sit on it and scream. He looked at a note which said 'Only you can find the GT'. He turned round to see a map of Mount Blarg. He went there to find it was totally dark. He found a human and hypnotised him to tell him where the Golden Toilet was. Once he had found it he sucked its golden powers and turned round, 'I am powerful *muahaha!*' said the devil evilly.

Umairah Mehmood (9)
Killinghall Primary School, Bradford

Mini Saga Story

Once upon a time in a land far, far away there was a crazy creature called Slime Head and another crazy creature called Poo Head who were fighting. Slimey Eyeball Head called the police because they were fighting. There was another crazy creature called Doofy and he arrested Poo Head and shot him with a fart blaster. It was Christmas and Poo Head destroyed Christmas and he changed into the Grinch.

The next day Poo Head, Doofy and Slimey Eyeball Head died. The police station was bombed forever.

Dawud Ahmed (9)
Killinghall Primary School, Bradford

The Bog-Eyed Monster

The Bog-Eyed Monster is so mischievous. The Bog-Eyed Monster would not want to know what happened. He wears make-up under the bed. He always lies and never tells the truth. He is very naughty. He never ever listens to anyone. He hates the food he has to eat. He has not changed at all. He is still a very horrible pet. He bites some people's bums and then they scream so loud that the neighbours hear and then knock on the door or ring the police. Because he is screaming they do not answer the door...

Kanzul Imaan (10)
Killinghall Primary School, Bradford

The Underworld Of Darkness

This is Devil Dave he lives in Og Bog. He likes blood. Once in Og Bog Devil Dave got lost. He fell in a cave and Big Cyclops came and attacked him. He said, 'Help! help!' No one came so he fought him. Luckily his friend came and saved him. Devil Dave went to Earth because someone died, then he heard that no one died but he still went to Earth. Everyone gave him presents and his friend gave him a gold segway. He went to the park every day and played with it. He'll never forget that day.

Sohaib Hussain (9)
Killinghall Primary School, Bradford

The Annoying Orange Devil

On a dark and miserable night the Annoying Orange Devil sneaked into a stall of different fruit and veg. As quick as a flash a lady came to buy him and took him to her house. It was a very long journey but he reached there in thirty minutes. When they were there the lady put him in a very big fruit basket straight away and left him there until she wanted to eat him. He said to himself, 'Where will I go? I can't get out of here!' He ran to the door but where would he go...?

Amna Bahadar (10)
Killinghall Primary School, Bradford

The Incident

Once there was a creature under the toilet seat. He had a dragon-like tail and two big eyes. Straight away Tom found him in the bin. The next day, the family went to clean the dirty toilet but the toilet cleaner went on him, he needed to get dirty. He jumped in the bin and he felt better. After that he learned he shouldn't sting people but he did it anyway. So, next time you go to the toilet take a hammer and toilet cleaner unless you want to be the next victim of Stinky Mac Stinkweed.

Armaan Hussain (10)
Killinghall Primary School, Bradford

Slime Eyes' Mystery Mission

Have you met Slime Eyes? In the middle of a desert Slime Eyes was getting ready for a party but when he came out of his cave he got attacked. All of a sudden when Slime Eyes woke up he was in a dark room. When the door opened monsters were surrounding the door. Slime Eyes didn't like this. Slime Eyes went tiny and ran.

A few days later he got a letter and the monsters asked him what it said. Slime Eyes got angry and went to jump off the top of a mountain but he got saved.

Laiyba Hussain (9)
Killinghall Primary School, Bradford

Spikey Ray Doesn't Go On Holiday

One day Spikey Ray was going on holiday so he packed all his stuff but there was a strange noise coming from outside. It was his parents, they left for the airport because they thought he was in the car. Spikey Ray was by himself and he did not know what to do. He got really scared and thought it was a dream but it wasn't. It was real. He thought of going to the next-door neighbour and they were at home so he stayed there until his parents came back to their house.

Alimurtaza Arfan (9)

Killinghall Primary School, Bradford

Queen Flame Thrower And The Menacing Ice

Queen Flame Thrower was in her castle having a tour and saw a bit of ice. She looked out of the window and saw her people freezing. She went to investigate and found she couldn't melt the ice. She then figured out it was Ice Guy's doing. She was carefully treading the icy land avoiding the icy water. In the mist she could see three icicles holding her wand. Then she remembered she had power to melt the ice. So she melted the ice and then nothing bothered her.

Eiman Kauser (9)
Killinghall Primary School, Bradford

Scary Clown

One day there lived an alien called Destroyer. He could change into a human. The next day he saw that a person and another person were fighting, he came out and they saw him and became a gang. Suddenly a UFO came. There stood the Boggle Monster who took the Destroyer. The police came but didn't help. They went to Uranus but a letter soon came and said the Killer Clown was coming for them. They looked out of the window and there stood the Killer Clown...

Usman Qaiser (10)
Killinghall Primary School, Bradford

Yaz

Yaz was a fifteen-year-old boy and he loved to stay underground. One day he was thinking what could he do. He had no friends to play with. He said, 'What can I do?' Then he remembered there were trails where he lived so he could play all by himself. He did not need friends anymore. He followed the first trail and it led to a kitchen. The next trail was to where he lived.

The next day he woke up and he had friends to play with.

Azaan Sarfraz (9)

Killinghall Primary School, Bradford

Untitled

Marshmallow Land is a bit dirty and a bit clean but there is a boy called Marshmallow Boy. He is very dirty. If he sees anyone who's clean he gets very angry. He saw a person watching and they were clean so he got angry. He went up to them and told them to wear some dirty clothes and if they didn't listen to him he would turn them into a marshmallow. Marshmallow Boy was very happy because everyone was dirty.

Suleman Ali (9)
Killinghall Primary School, Bradford

Snaty Paty Returns

One day a villain called Snaty Paty came to a fair and Gaglley saw him. 'How did you get here?' said Gaglley.

Snaty Paty replied, 'By a spaceship!'

Gaglley tried to get Snaty Paty but he was too fast. The clever Gaglley used his ten eyes to spot evil Snaty Paty. Still he could not spot him. Of course, Snaty Paty was inside the sewer. The brave Gaglley got into the sewer and captured Snaty Paty and that was the end of him. Gaglley went on holiday and Snaty Paty was locked up. That was the end of the evil.

Khadija Abdelbadir (7)

Paradise Primary School, Dewsbury

The Monster And The Boy

Once upon a time there was a monster and he went to a little boy's house. The boy saw him and said, 'Who are you?'
'I am a monster,' he said.
'I don't like monsters.'
'I will help you with everything,' said the monster.
The boy said, 'My mum helps me.'
The monster said, 'I will help you tidy your room.'
The boy said, 'OK I'll deal with it!'
The monster said he would and the boy thought it was great.
Then the monster had to go home and the boy was sad.

Umaama Ali (7)
Paradise Primary School, Dewsbury

Slimy Slimy Big

One day Slimy turned into a gigantic monster with ten legs, gigantic wings, marble hair, enormous spiky eyes and enormous ears, he was hideous.
One day his friend said, 'How did you get like that?'
'I don't know,' Slimy said.
He went back home and the next day he was more gigantic. He had spectacular eyes, spiky hair, slimy wings and was green and brilliant. Then he went back to his friend's house and his friend didn't say anything. He went back home and became tall, massive and with gigantic feet.

Aisha Bodhania (6)
Paradise Primary School, Dewsbury

Poisonous Betty

Long ago there was a crazy monster called Poisonous Betty and she went to see her parents so she flew to Fire Monster Land and she saw her parents. Betty loved it. She went across the road to her grandma's house and she had lunch and her grandpa gave her a present. It was a watch. 'Thank you,' said Poisonous Betty.
Then Betty went to town and she saw her friend, Rose, and they had some food at a restaurant. They had fun all day. When it was night-time they went to bed and dreamed all night.

Zainab Vali (6)
Paradise Primary School, Dewsbury

Petty Horny And Horny Horny

Petty Horny was in Monster Land to see her cousin called Horny Horny. He said, 'Let's go to the beach,' and Petty Horny said, 'No.'
Horny Horny asked her why and she said she was going back home to Giant Land. Horny Horny asked if he could take her and she said she could go by herself. He asked if she was walking with her giant feet and she said she was going by train. She was going to see her mummy who wasn't well. Horny Horny asked her to tell her mum he hoped she would be better soon.

Hafsa Tukur (7)
Paradise Primary School, Dewsbury

Jelly Hands

Long ago and far away on Planet Bong there lived a spotty, naughty, hairy, long-tongued, five-eyed monster. The monster was called Jelly Hands. One day Jelly Hands went to visit Planet Earth and when she got there she saw a little boy. Jelly Hands didn't like humans but instead of killing the boy she ate him. Then she saw there was a party and there were more humans so she ate them too! But then she was very ill and she puked and all the humans came out.

Fatima Moosa (7)
Paradise Primary School, Dewsbury

The Dino Rex And The Invisible Spider

Once upon a time there was a dino rex and the dino rex hated spiders. He knocked on Invisible Spider's door so Invisible Spider opened the door. The dino rex said, 'Hello, I've come to eat you up.' 'What!' said Invisible Spider.

The next morning the dino rex thought he should not eat Invisible Spider and he should say sorry to him. He went round and said sorry to Invisible Spider and they lived happily ever after.

Ahmed Musa Shoaib (6)
Paradise Primary School, Dewsbury

A Nosey Day

In a cottage made out of slime was a monster called NH which was the nickname for Nosey Head. One day, the queen came to collect some jewels and Nosey Head had hidden them because he knew the queen was coming.

One day, he was having a shower and he heard a drilling noise. He quickly finished and took the drill off the person and he got killed. The next day NH was in peace because he had learned not to be nosy. Good! He had learned his lesson.

Humayra Patel (7)
Paradise Primary School, Dewsbury

The Crazy Scally

Once there was a monster called Scally. He was going for a walk and on the way he met three clowns and they juggled for him and made him laugh a lot. He was very happy to be there. He was so busy laughing he didn't see an ant come at the back of his hair. Then he was very itchy and he couldn't stop laughing. It was so funny that he was pulling a face. He lived happily ever after.

Maariyah Moosa (6)
Paradise Primary School, Dewsbury

King Slimy Vs The Enormous Ray

One dark night King Slimy was cleaning the streets and he was making them clean. The Enormous Ray was always putting dirt on the street but King Slimy was always there to stop him. Enormous Ray had new plans.

The next day King Slimy saw there were piles of dirt but he was able to manage to eat all the dirt so he defeated Enormous Ray and he never came back again.

Muhammad Patel (6)

Paradise Primary School, Dewsbury

Interplanetary War

There is an interplanetary war. Bombg is a captain of Armbomb Planet Army. His sworn enemy is Sorr, a small planet of shape-shifters light years away. During a space battle Bombg's army was wiped out. Bombg crash-lands on Sorr but he survives and must hide. The aliens of Sorr are made of bubbles but can look like any other creature. Bombg is an armbomber, they are small and hairy and have horns. Bombg pretends he is from Sorr and he has shape-shifted as an armbomber. He steals a ship and flies home.

Kian Joe Salisbury (11)
Springwell Leeds Primary Academy, Leeds

Deserted

One day Zayjung was stuck on an island with nothing to do but wait. He waited a long time but as usual, no one came. He got really annoyed and trudged around the island with his boat-like feet and shouted at the top of his lungs, 'I want to die!' I think someone heard him because, the next thing you know, he was in a Concorde flying through space at warp speed. He wanted to go to Advertureye leaving absolutely nothing at all, not even a grain of absolutely anything.

Konneur James Dooley (11)
Springwell Leeds Primary Academy, Leeds

Tom The Hero

It was a nice day and a nice boy called Tom was playing outside when suddenly the sun went in. It was dark. The sun disappeared and in its place was a spaceship. An alien got out. It was looking for Tom so he could get rid of all the boys on Earth. The alien found Tom and sucked him up in the spaceship. Tom found that he had magic powers and could use an invisible crowbar to get him and all the other boys free. Tom steered the spaceship to Earth and they were all free.

James T Sheridan (9)

Springwell Leeds Primary Academy, Leeds

When Hairy Met Sun

Hairy came back to Planet Earth scared but excited that he might be blown back to his planet. Finally he said, 'I'm here.' But after two hours he was there but everything was different. 'What is that bright thing?' said Hairy. 'Is that what they call the sun? Oh no it burns so much. Oh no I'm melting. Oh no!'

Lewis Fletcher (9)
Springwell Leeds Primary Academy, Leeds

Grizzly Gurgle King Of Pluto

One dazzling space night Zargle thought he was the ruler of Saturn and Pluto. Someone needed to be in charge. So that night he gathered the names of both planets. He picked a name 'Gurgle'.
The next morning the sun was shining and he announced that Gurgle was in charge.
Zargle got jealous because everyone liked him. So when Gurgle ate breakfast (worm brains with salt), he arrived saying, 'I want to kill you.' However Gurgle had no weapons so he got salt and sprinkled it on top of him. Finally Zargle melted. Aliens named him 'King Gurgle of Pluto'.

Aamna Ali (9)
Victoria Primary School, Keighley

Speedy Meets Big Eyed Yeti

Speedy was on a day run and he came upon a big eyed yeti. Yeti was a huge monstrous shape-shifter and he challenged Speedy to a race. As Speedy was about to run, Yeti hit the leg of Speedy. 'Ow!' said Speedy.
Yeti ran for the finish line.
Speedy managed to cure himself and ran at the speed of light and he crossed the finish line before Yeti.
'Roar!' growled Yeti as he smashed a cherry puff rock. 'I'll get you Speedy,' he shouted.
'You'll never catch me!' said Speedy and off he went.

Uthman Ali (10)
Victoria Primary School, Keighley

The Revenge Of The Deadly Dogie Demon

There was once a mean and nasty monster called The Deadly Dogie Demon. He was so selfish that he even locked two of his enemies in a dungeon. He was so evil that even elephants would get knocked out by him. Once he was in a shop and a monster called Squishy bumped into him. The Deadly Dogie Demon dragged Squishy into the scary and dark dungeon. Then Squishy said, 'Please, I am scared of the dark.'
'Oh be quiet,' shouted the nasty demon. The monster in the street made a plan and he was never seen again.

Alisha Zafran (9)
Victoria Primary School, Keighley

Fries!

Toote Mc Goo landed on Earth and he teleported to the market and saw all the food from around the world. He saw curries, croissants, cookies, so many kinds of food. Then he saw his favourite food at Freddy's Fries. He said, 'Freddy can I have some fries?'

Freddy saw that the monster wasn't scary and he said, 'Go away Monster and come back when you have some money!'

As soon as he heard that he was off. He made a plan to get some money. At last he got the money and the fries and he went home happy.

Benyamin Malik (9)

Victoria Primary School, Keighley

Crazy Shifter Gets A Taste Of His Own Medicine

Once upon a dream there was a scary monster called Crazy Shifter. His face was red and his body was green. Crazy Shifter decided he wanted to prank the most cruel teacher in the school, Mrs Blood Thirsty. He left pots of blood on the teacher's desk because she was a vampire. Once she drank all of it she had to go to the toilet. Crazy Shifter shape-shifted to look like her and said to the students the class was over. Mrs Blood Thirsty saw him shape-shift and he had to collect blood for her every day from then on.

Ehsan Khurshid (10)

Victoria Primary School, Keighley

Nine Eyed Bogey Eater

There was a crazy creature who was called Nine Eyed Bogey Eater. He eats bogies for breakfast, lunch and dinner. He also lives in a green house and everything is green.

One day Nine Eyed Bogey Eater was playing when his snot came out, he had nothing to clean his nose with so when no one was looking he ate it. Ever since then Nine Eyed Bogey Eater has been eating bogies. He says they are the best thing to eat. Now he is famous and has stopped eating bogies and he eats orange crayons and drinks blue ink.

Mishal Hussain (9)
Victoria Primary School, Keighley

Untitled

Once upon a time there was a very bad creature called Hairy Beast Monster. He was powerful and speedy and no one could get him because he was too fat. He kept on making hammers and smashing towns but he kept on running round the world. Then he got a huge hammer. Both of his brothers were annoying him so he just ignored them. People kept on throwing eggs and he was really upset because his face was shaped like an egg. Then his opponent got a bouncy thing and jumped on his head.

Muhammad Ismail (9)
Victoria Primary School, Keighley

Clever Bob In School

There was a monster named Bob, he was very clever and he was gooey. He really wanted to go to school. He was from Mars and he hated water because he thought he would go blue because he was green. One day he went to school and they let him in. He did so much work. He always tried hard at everything his teacher gave him to do. He never did his homework at home. He was always second in class. One day he tried his best at his homework and he got it all right. Then he was first.

Aaliyah Jamil (9)
Victoria Primary School, Keighley

Being Best Friends

One day Crazy Dragon and Crazy Dog became best friends at school. They grew up together and did everything together. They played at school and at home. Then Crazy Dragon saw Crazy Dog had made a new friend called Spot and he was angry. He moved away with his family and lived somewhere else. Days went by and Crazy Dragon became more upset. Then they decided to talk and realised they would always be best friends and stay like that forever!

Adam Hussain (10)
Victoria Primary School, Keighley

A Monster In My House

Once upon a time a boy went out to the shop and there was a pink and scary monster in his house. His mum didn't know he'd gone out and she didn't know about the monster. The monster jumped out and his mum was very scared. But then the boy came back and he frightened the monster away. His mum said, 'I didn't know you were out. Where did you go?'
The boy answered, 'I was just outside.'

Juwairiyah Mahmood (9)
Victoria Primary School, Keighley

YoungWriters
Est.1991

YOUNG WRITERS INFORMATION

We hope you have enjoyed reading this book – and that you will continue to in the coming years.

If you're a young writer who enjoys reading and creative writing, or the parent of an enthusiastic poet or story writer, do visit our website **www.youngwriters.co.uk**. Here you will find free competitions, workshops and games, as well as recommended reads, a poetry glossary and our blog.

If you would like to order further copies of this book, or any of our other titles, then please give us a call or visit **www.youngwriters.co.uk**.

Young Writers
Remus House
Coltsfoot Drive
Peterborough
PE2 9BF
(01733) 890066
info@youngwriters.co.uk